71,500

The Complete and Utter History Of The World

The Complete and Utter History Of The World

by

Samuel Stewart

(aged 9)

Illustrations by Alex Fox

Published in 2013 by
Short Books
3A Exmouth House
Pine Street
EC1R 0JH

10 9 8 7 6 5 4 3 2 1

A CIP catalogue record for this book is available
from the British Library.

ISBN 978-1-78072-183-5

Printed and bound in Great Britain by
CPI Group (UK) Ltd, Croydon, CR0 4YY

Cover illustration by Alex Fox
Cover design by nathanburtondesign.com

Dear Mrs Stewart,

I thought I had better write to you in advance of prize-giving day, to explain why Samuel is not receiving the History prize (Under 10s), which personally I think he deserves. But: no names, no pack drill! Who am I to argue with the Powers That Be?!

Suffice it to say that Sam's compendious 'History of the World' (which I enclose) is written with what I consider exceptional enthusiasm and interest, and coming in at ten times the length of any other entry, should have won hands down, no contest, on evidence of endurance alone.

However, the PTB have taken issue with some of his factual infelicities and have unaccountably preferred Chardonnay Smith's (in my view fanciful) essay entitled 'Tear-Stained Ration-Coupons: The Tale of a Wartime Evacuee'.

I just want you to know that whatever path Sam takes in the future, he has very nice handwriting for a boy.

I understand from Sam that he is now embarking on 'The Entire World and Everything In It', and wish his next teacher extremely good luck with this.

Yours sincerely,

Nancy Cooper
Class Teacher Year 5

P.S. I have only corrected some of his spellings, which were quite enough.

Contents

Introduction

The first and most important thing to know about History is that it is very old. History goes back a very long way indeed. In fact, the very first people on Earth, the Cave Men, probably didn't even realise that History was starting, otherwise they would have invented writing a bit more quickly and begun writing it down.

So, History had to wait quite a long time before anyone started writing it down, because nobody really noticed it was there.

The other thing you need to know about History is that people do not agree about what it really is. For example, there are at least two versions of how History began and they are both highly suspicious. Did God create Adam and Eve or did we evolve from walking fish? I think not. From this alone it is clear that many historians are just making up what they don't know.

The Ancient
Egyptians

As Mrs Cooper says, the clue is often in the title. Their name tells us that the Ancient Egyptians were Ancient and from Egypt, where they lived in Pyramids. Pyramids are like the opposite of a Tardis – they are very big on the outside and very small on the inside, so the Ancient Egyptians had to walk sideways to get through the narrow corridors and tunnels. To save time they walked sideways all the time, as pictures prove.

We only know about them because Pyramids are very sturdy and some have still not fallen down, but mainly because the Ancient Egyptians finally invented writing, so History could begin properly. Ancient Egyptian writing had pictures instead of words, so was not really writing but drawing – something many historians seem not to have noticed, I might add. This was very time-consuming, especially if the word was a very hard one to draw, like History. A word like History might take a year to draw, but a word like Pyramid would take no time at all and Snake would be really easy.

Worse, although they had invented paper, they had not yet invented pens, so at first they had to do their writing carved on stones which took ages. Fortunately the Ancient Egyptians had loads of slaves – probably about a hundred – so they got them to do all the carving so they could get on with their Maths, which they were also busy inventing. The most famous Maths they invented was Pythagoras' Theorum. (Try writing that in pictures! I don't think so!) Pythagoras was probably trying to build a new Pyramid because he was very interested in triangles, but they kept coming out wrong. He was trying to think Outside The Box, which you have to when you are doing really hard Maths, (especially if there are Brackets), when he had the brilliant idea of Squaring a Hippopotamus and this, amazingly, gave him his answer.

Other things the Ancient Egyptians invented

were: The River Nile, Moses baskets and Cleopatra's Needle. Moses baskets were used for floating babies in the River Nile, which seems to have been a popular sport. Cleopatra is the second most famous Ancient Egyptian, after Tutankhamen. Tutankhamen was a Boy King and this is probably why Ancient Egypt was so Great, with brilliant things like triangular houses and baby-floating races, which a grown-up would never think of. Cleopatra was famous because although she had Rome At Her Feet, which must have been quite inconvenient (although walking sideways would probably be really helpful here), she was a Great Queen.

She was also very kind, sending presents everywhere, and sent her famous Needle to England. (Don't go thinking this is a real needle – it's a tall pointy stone called a Basilisk.) In England the people (who were still in the Stone Age) liked it very much, as it was made of their favourite material: Stone. But didn't know what it was for, so they put it up in London where it has been used as an Ornament ever since. Cleopatra sadly was killed when one of her pet snakes bit her. (That would have been quite easy to write in pictures, though, so is probably how we know.)

The other thing the Ancient Egyptians invented were Mummies, which they kindly sent to nearly every museum in the world, along with Artefacts, which they sent as a game. They would send an Artefact to a museum and everyone had to guess what it was. They were very good at this game as museums today have Ancient Egyptian Artefacts on display and have still not worked out what all of them are.

After a while, Ancient Egyptians had invented everything they needed and History moved to...

Ancient Greece

The Ancient Greeks were again very old and lived in Greece. They invented Proper Writing which was quite urgent as they were trying to invent Poetry at the same time and you can only remember so many poems.

Unfortunately, no one had thought of inventing Reading, so people would look at the mysterious curly writing and nod sagely until Reading was Discovered – it's now so famous it has a town named after it. (Historians will insist on arguing about which was invented first: Reading or Writing anwd say it is a Chicken-and-Egg Situation, which they often say when they don't know the answer.)

The Ancient Greeks seem to have had a lot of time on their hands as they also invented Philosophy. This involved thinking a lot and then suddenly having a brilliant idea. Sometimes they did their thinking in a barrel and sometimes in the bath.

When they suddenly had a brilliant idea they would leap up and shout 'Urethra!' (this is Greek) to let everyone know that they were really doing their job and not just having a bath.

They also invented some useful things, like Archimedes' Screw, which could move water uphill which was much more modern than making slaves do it. All these labour-saving devices gave them more time for the Philosophy and they also invented Hummous and Taramasalata and Pitta Bread, so they could have dips while they were doing the important thinking, which always helps.

They also invented loads of gods. The top god was Zeus, who opened Pandora's Box and found the Olympic Games inside – another great Greek invention. The first Olympic Games were held on Mount Olympus which was very inconvenient for other countries to get to, so even though they were Ancient, the Greeks won everything. This made the Tunic Wars happen, and eventually everyone agreed that the world would share the Olympic Games and take it in turns to have them in a very hard-to-get-to place, making it fair.

The Greeks were quite good at wars, but used to make the women do all the work. One woman called Helen was made to launch a thousand ships on her own *using just her face*. This seems quite cruel but we have to remember the famous saying that 'When the Past is in another country, they do things differently there.' The Greeks also had a very rough lot of people called Tartans. When the Tartans had a baby they would put it on a hillside. If it didn't roll off in the night, they would keep it.

They also invented the Parthenon, a very long running race. The story goes that a messenger had to carry a very important message to somewhere called Parthenon, get the answer and run all the way back again without stopping. He managed it but unfortunately forgot the answer. The Greeks remembered that you must never shoot the messenger, so turned it into a sport instead. (In future they decided to write all messages down – which they now could – to be on the safe side.)

Later on, someone had a 'Urethra' moment and got the brilliant idea of sending messages on horseback and created a crack unit of postmen for priority deliveries (The Four Horsemen of the Acropolis). The Greeks loved horses and made great big statues of them as well as painting them on the tiniest toys, such as the Elgin Marbles. They had quite a lot of wars with the Trojans and because the Trojans knew the Greeks had a soft spot for horses, they made the Greeks a great big wooden horse as a present, leading to the popular saying: You should *always* look in a gift horse's mouth (to see if there are any enemy soldiers hiding in there).

The Greeks also invented Democracy, where everyone got to vote about what laws they would have instead of one person just making them up. The Philosophers of course had a head start here, having done all that thinking already. So, while everyone else was still scratching their heads and looking for a pencil, the first thing they did was to invent a law that only people they liked could vote, and this didn't include slaves, women and people who didn't like Philosophy.

The Greeks had now invented everything important and could get on with their thinking and making up new gods while History moved to...

Ancient Rome

Ancient Rome was probably the cleverest of the Ancient Civilisations, as it went round taking what everyone else had invented, leaving it free to invent luxuries like underfloor heating and ice cream. They were also very crafty. For example, they didn't have any gods, and they liked Ancient Greece's gods, but didn't want any trouble with the Greeks, so they simply borrowed the Greeks' gods and quickly made copies of them and gave them all new names – much better and more modern ones like Jupiter and Mars. Then they put all the Greek gods back before the Greeks noticed anything suspicious was going on.

The Romans were much better and more modern than everyone else in History so far in nearly every way. They liked the Ancient Egyptians' Pharaohs who ruled everyone with Dissolute Power but they also liked the Greeks' Democracy, so they decided to have both. Their rulers were called Emperor or Caesar but they also had a Senate where Caesar pretended other people could have a say, but then did what he wanted anyway. (This is known as The Art of Compromise.) The most famous Caesar was Julius. Julius Caesar is famous for:

(1) Inventing a famous salad;

(2) Building a Palace in Las Vegas (the first Roman Emperor to do so);

(3) Killing his wife with a lemon squeezer;

(4) Being murdered outside the Houses of Parliament by the Ides of March, a gang who included Mark Antony and Ettu Brutus, because all three had fallen under the spell of the Serpent of the Nile, otherwise known as Cleopatra, giver of basilisks.

Other important Caesars were:

🖐 Caligula who was born mad

🖐 Nero who went mad later

🖐 Claudius who had a mad wife

Samuel Stewart (aged 9)

So it is easy to see why Julius was the best Caesar. He also built a lot of roads and made them all lead to Rome. This was a bit confusing when trying to leave Rome, but at least all the Roman soldiers who had been away conquering could always find their way home again.

The Romans were very good at writing and by now had invented proper letters, not all the curly stuff the Greeks used that no one else could understand. Everyone else in the world agreed theirs was the best alphabet, and copied it.

(Except for the Arabs, who kept Arabic, and the Hebrews, who kept Hebrew, and although both have similar languages, the Arabs and Hebrews are generally agreed to be Mutually Unintelligible.)

(And also except for the Russians who have stuck with an Acrylic Alphabet.)

The Romans were Great because they had an enormous army that they kept sending to get new countries to be part of the Roman Empire. Sometimes they had too many soldiers, so they fed them to the lions at the Coliseum. They

also fed the lions some Early Christians they didn't know what to do with, as they refused to worship the brilliant gods they had 'invented', and kept drawing fish everywhere instead of using the super new alphabet the Romans had invented.

Eventually Jesus Christ himself came along (this was the person the Christians had been waiting for) and the Romans called him King of the Jews just to annoy the Christians. The Romans *did* get Jesus in the end, but it took them a long time as King Harold had failed to get him when he was a baby. That time, fortunately, him and Mary and Joseph were saved by Pontius Pilot who got them on the famous Flight Into Egypt and explained he had just been washing his hands so Harold wouldn't wonder where he had been.

When Jesus had grown up the Romans killed him in what seems a horrible way to us, but was quite normal for Romans. ('When the Past is in another country, etc.') Anyway, it didn't do the Romans any good because more and more people started agreeing with the Christians, and eventually they had a new leader: The Holy Roman Umpire, now known as The Pope.

The best thing the Romans did was to discover...

Ancient Briton

A bit like History, no one knew Briton was there, except the Vikings. Briton was still in the Stone Age because every time they invented something decent the Vikings came raving and pillaging and broke it. The Romans were much better because, as we have seen, they only borrowed things, and they also took their own cool stuff everywhere. The Britons were led by the Ice Queen Boudicca, who was a Great Worrier. She was worried that because there was nothing worth borrowing from Briton the Romans probably wanted to borrow Briton itself – how right she was! Boudicca fought the Romans with a tripod and had a big shield with a Union Jack on for luck and spikes on her chariot wheels, but despite all this was no match for the crafty Romans, who invited her to negotiate peace and then melted her with underfloor heating.

The Romans were nice to the Britons after that, because they thought they were angels. The

Britons didn't let on of course and let the Romans carry on like they owned the place, giving every-thing new names, building roads to Rome, etc. for a quiet life. This is called Appeasement, and you do it when you can't win, instead of losing.

Once the Romans had arrived Briton started becoming Great as well. The Roman soldiers started marrying the British women and pretty soon discovered they weren't really angels, but by then it was fortunately too late, of course. Their children were half-and-half, so soon you couldn't tell who was a Roman and who was a Briton and there was no more trouble. This inter-marriage became known as *'rite de seigneur'* which is Roman for 'right to say no' and meant no one had to do anything they didn't want to. Briton carried this on to nowadays in the form of Public Opinion, which is: although people have voted for someone to be in charge they can still complain about them doing it all wrong. This is part of what makes Briton Great.

The British Romans also invented Fair Play, which is a great British tradition, and means that it doesn't matter who wins anything, as long as it was Fair. This was brilliant for Briton, as when they won anything it was Really Great and when they lost it Didn't Matter. The Roman Britons were fairly pleased about having no strife and conflict, and in future Briton decided if it had any wars it would try to have them abroad.

However, they had one last war at home that led to...

The Norman Congress

By this time Briton had King Harold (not the same one who put Jesus on a cross and petrified him) and everything was ticking over nicely. So nicely, in fact, that King Norman of France looked across the English Channel (or *La Mancha*, as the French called it) and thought he would like to be king of it as well. The Norman Congress took quite a long time happening as the French soldiers did not like the look of British hotels, so every time they stopped somewhere for the night they built their own castle. First these were made of wood and were called Mott and Hoople Castles. Then they realised wooden castles were quite flammable and angry British hoteliers kept burning them down. So they built stone ones instead, which the Britons liked, on account of their fond memories of the Stone Age.

The Britons, just like they had with the Romans, decided to share nicely with the French (this is known as 'The Path of Least French Resistance') and when King Harold got an apple stuck in his eye they let Norman be king of Briton as well as France. That began the Norman Congress, which proved to be the Mother of all Parliaments. It also began a love affair between the Britons and the French on which the sun has never shone. After that, whenever France had an enemy (provided it wasn't Briton), Briton was right there At Her Side, and *visa-visa*, when Briton had an enemy (provided it wasn't France), France was Right Behind Her.

There was then quite a long Gap in History before...

The Middle Ages

The Middle Ages was so called because it was half way after The Dark/Stone Age and the Age when it began to be named, which Then thought it was Now, and therefore Modern, but was really Then, so it should properly be called the Quarter-of-the-Way-to-Now Ages, but let's not mince pies. The point is that everything started getting a bit nearer being Modern. (For example, Henry IV was the last badly-drawn King of Briton.)

In the Middle Ages, everyone was a bit depressed and wondering what was the meaning of life and wishing they were younger. To cheer them up a stand-up comedian (then called a poet) called Jeffrey Chortler would take them on pilgrimages and tell them funny stories on the way. (Actually some of the stories were not that funny and quite hard to under-stand, but the Middle Agers didn't mind, as it was better than being at home staring in the mirror, wondering what was it all for, and why bother, etc.)

The Middle Ages are also known for a group called the Medi-Evils, who were a rough lot and invented boiling oil, thumbscrews, leeches and hose. People only put up with them because they also invented Middle English, as before that everyone had been talking a mixture of Briton, Roman and French. The invention of Middle English was a great relief to everyone, especially Jeffrey Chortler, who up until then had to tell each story in three languages, and a pilgrimage is only so long and tourists can be quite impatient.

The invention of Middle English led to a flowering of poetry everywhere. Everywhere anyone looked there was a poem growing, and now everyone could understand it. British Literature turned out to be the Best Ever, and remains so to this date. And even Jeffrey Chortler, tour guide to the Middle Agers, was destined to become the Best Known Writer the Britons had never read.

The Tudors

The Tudors were the best royal dynasty so far and were mostly Henrys and the most important Henry was the eighth one. In those days most boys were named after their fathers, and because King Henry (who didn't need a number, because then he was the Only Henry) had eight sons he named them all Henry, adding a number to save confusion. Mysteriously, all of the first seven Henrys died (although they all dutifully completed their reigns), leaving only the Henry the Eighth, or Henry VIII as he should properly be called (because although everyone was now writing in English they were still counting in Roman).

To make up for all his dead brothers, Henry VIII married all their wives and so had six (although maths is not my strongest point, one clearly did not live long enough to even get a wife, or perhaps she died in childbirth, which lots of women did in those days, maybe because

Commonsense had not yet been invented and sometimes even babies got thrown out with the bathwater by mistake).

He did not, of course, marry them all at once, as that would have been obviously against the law, so they took it in turns. (This is just as well as three of them were called Catherine and no one wants to start numbering their wives, as Mum says when Dad says 'spag bol again?')

However, in those days it was quite tricky to be married six times as the law was quite old-fashioned of course, and ordinary people were not allowed any divorces but rich people could have a maximum of two (unlike today, when most people can have as many divorces as they like, as Mum reminds Dad when he says 'spag bol again?' *again*).

So poor Henry VIII had to get through six wives but was only allowed two divorces, which was tricky number-wise. He used these up on the most fragrant wives: Catherine of Tarragon and Anne of Cloves. Fortunately another wife died of her own accord (Jane Seymour, a notorious actress), and one wife outlived Henry VIII (Catherine

Samuel Stewart (aged 9)

Part), and two got accidentally beheaded – these were Anne Berlin and Catherine Howodd and whose reputations were later reviled by Posterity. (Which is always a good thing in History.)

Even with six wives at his perusal, Henry VIII was not a very good father. Most of his children were never born, or didn't survive (see baby/bathwater confusion above) and even amongst the ones that did survive there was unfold trouble.

They were: Mary Queen of Scots and Elizabeth Queen of Everything Else. When you think these were the children of his first two wives, quite a lot of trouble could have been avoided with the other four, but he couldn't have known that then and we are looking at History with the Benefit Of Hindsight, which is like having wing mirrors while you are charging through History backwards (or in advance, depending).

Elizabeth was clearly the right one to be Queen of Everything, as History went on to prove, as Mary Queen of Scots was very annoying and doing darning all the time and locking herself up in a castle, making plots and being a Catholic. In the end Elizabeth had to arrange for Mary to have an 'accidental' beheading but this was not kept as quiet as it should have been as Mary had a little dog which lived under her skirts and when she had her 'accident' it ran out and rolled over and died for the queen and everyone clapped quite noisily. Mary had had a little baby boy who she had held over the battlements for the people to see (like Michael Jackson did, but she didn't get told off like he did – Health and Safety different, when the past is in another country, etc.) but he too was probably thrown out with the bathwater, leaving the path clear for Elizabeth to be the First Proper English Queen since Bouddica, and unlike Boudicca, played the Virginals.

Elizabeth I was England's first Virginal Monarch, and thus led to an outbreak of creativity everywhere. Anywhere you looked, there was a madrigal growing, and in London, especially, there was a severe outbreak of Shakespeare.

Even though Elizabeth was quite clearly a Tudor, she was so populous that her era (or Age) became known as Elizabethan. Plus, if you thought Henry VIII wives' dresses were on the large side, just wait till you see Elizabeth's dresses. They were so big she could bestride the Globe, and did! (No dogs there, though. Elizabeth I famously never allowed any men, let alone dogs, to besmirch her virtue – otherwise known as underskirt or petticoat.)

The Elizabethan Age became so popular on its own account that it gave rise to a group who laughed at everything Tudor, called the Mock Tudors. They were very clever and built houses that were mostly like Tudor houses but mainly had a funny or ironic bit which was not really Tudor but only a cheap imitation of it and might fall down if you leant on it. They found this hilarious, and it got the real/authentic Tudors really mad. (The way to tell if a house is really Tudor or only Mock Tudor is: is it whole-timbered? If it is only half-timbered it is most probably Mock.)

William Shakespeare is the most famous of all the famous Elizabethans. But let's not forget the others. There was Sir Walter Raleigh who was famous because:

- he invented tobacco for which Customs and Excise were eternally grateful and so turned a blind eye to his invention of The Potato (see next item) which Dad reckons could have been more profitable to them in the long run,

- he saw the Spanish Armadillo on Plymouth Hoe and calmly just kept eating chips,

- he discovered the bicycle but then hid it until Mrs Penny Farthing rediscovered it much later, so never got the full credit.

But now let's get on to Shakespeare.

Since Jeffrey Chortler, saviour of the Middle Agers, everyone had been a bit rubbish at poetry. Then William Shakespeare came along and turned everything around. He was Utterly Brilliant and The Best Ever at doing plays and poems. His great strength was his virtuosity. But apart from being *so* virtuous *and* good at playing instruments, he was quite the genius at all different kinds of plays. He did comedies (where everyone gets married at the end), and tragedies (where everyone gets killed at the end) and, best of all, Histories (where depending on who wins at the end, people are either feeling quite happy or quite tragic, or are looking through their programmes or at their watches, because, as we know, History always takes longer than you hoped). You can't hurry History and just have to wait for it to finish sometimes.

Because Shakespeare was utterly brilliant in every way so far discovered, audiences would show their enjoyment of his plays by utterly dismantling the playhouses and imprisoning the actors until there was nothing left except His Words. They have stopped this kind of thing these days but there is still nothing left except His Words, and no eminence of his real existence anywhere.

This has led to a suppository that perhaps Shakespeare did not really write his plays but they were written by someone else of the same name.

However this situation has been happily presolved by Shakespearean scholars who have assured us (a) Shakespeare definitely did write everything and (b) Shakespeare was definitely who he thought he was. Phew! Everyone was immensely happy with that outcome, especially the town of Stratford-on-Avon, which otherwise might have had to move.

The only things we know for certain about Shakespeare, apart from that he certainly wrote his own material, are:

- He lived, to give it its full name, in Stratford-Upon-the-Bard-of-the-Swan-of-Avon, in Ann Hathaway's cottage, where he slept in her second-best bed – no one knows why.

- He was in love with a dark lady, which were quite rare at the time.

- He wrote some plays which most people think must be brilliant. Everyone knows about 'Romeo and Juliet', but he wrote some good ones too, such as:

Tragedies:

'Macbeth' (which you must never say in a theatre as it's bad luck and as a forfeit you have to watch the play).

'Hamlet' – Hamlet is a young partially sighted prince (e.g. 'Is this a dagger I see before me?' 'No, Hamlet', the audience wishes to cry out. 'It is the skull of your best friend, Nelson') who mainly asks himself lots of very hard questions which no one answers. This mostly proves Shakespeare was a Genius.

Comedies:

'All's Well That Ends In Much Ado About Nothing'

'Love's Labour's Lost If You Like It'

'The Taming of the Shrub'

History or King Plays:

Lots of ones about Kings, who often end up

unfortunately In Parts. The funniest one is apparently 'King Edward Lear'.

Farces:

'Julius Caesar, Anthony and Cleopatra' (aka 'The Hilarious Comedy of Errors')

'The Merchant of Venice' and the zany sequels 'The Two Gentlemen of Venice' and 'Othello (More of Venice)'.

Because Shakespeare is argumentatively our No. 1 National Treasure, his plays are still used as a punishment in schools. This is one of the many contradictions which make him so beloved by subsiding theatre. He remains the greatest Elizabethan and even Elizabeth I didn't mind by then because she was rotting away with Heavy Metal poisoning. This was on account of the cosmonauts she was recklessly applying to her face, brought on by still having to look like the Virginal Queen when she was way past playing them.

The Stuarts

The Stuarts were a very peculiar dynasty, namely because none of them were called Stuart, but mainly James or Charles and even Anne. Still, who am I to argue? And a king may look at a cabbage, etc. The Jameses were not that interesting and it only got exciting when there was a Charles on the throne (or *not* as we shall see)...

Charles I got into a lot of trouble with Parliament (which had by now been invented) and especially with the Puritans. This divided the country right down the middle. On the left everyone had to be a Puritan or a Parliamentarian or Roundhead. On the right everyone had to be Royal or Royalist (*like* a Royal, but not really one). So you could tell the difference when they had a battle (they hadn't got around to inventing uniforms yet), the ones on the left all dressed sensibly and the ones on the right all wore big hats, long hair and lots of lace.

Unsurprisingly, the Royalists were not very good at fighting (probably they had to keep stopping to look in the mirror, tie up ribbons, etc.), so the others won. Mrs Cooper says that the Puritans abolished fun, but I did some extra reading during German measles and in fact they did lots of worthwhile things like freedom of the press, sending all the boys to school, making women be Quakers, and spreading all the equality out more fairly, so it wasn't that they *abolished* fun, they just didn't have much time left over for it.

The leader of the Parliamentarians/Roundheads/Puritans/Sensibly-Dressed Party was Oliver Cromwell. Although he had abolished the monarchy and made sure Charles I had a fatal accident with an axe in the Banqueting Hall, he was soon suspiciously acting quite like a King himself, but it was too late now and everyone just had to put up with him, 'warps and all'.

Eventually the Royalists, who had all fled abroad with Charles I's son (who would have been the next king if Oliver Cromwell hadn't made kings illegal), cunningly sent malaria germs to kill Old Oliver. It worked, but clever Old Oliver also had a trick up his dead man's sleeve: his son, who then became Not King, just like Oliver had been Not King. Unfortunately, his son turned out to be a very poor Not King – even worse than Charles I – and soon everyone was wanting a proper Real King again.

The old King's son, Charles II, had been in Europe all this time, growing his hair, and was now a man. Britons said they were sorry about all the civil wars and revolution and chopping his dad's head off and everything and invited him back to be a Real King again. He said OK, but only if you promise not to cut my head off; and they said, OK but only if you are a better king than your dad and listen to Parliament. Then Charles II thought for a bit and said OK.

The best thing the new King did was decide that everyone *did* now have time for Fun and Lots Of It. The most important new law he made was about Fun, and it was to open up the theatres again (which the Puritans had shut because Shakespeare was definitely dead by then so plays were rubbish again, and what's the point, etc.) and make women go in them.

In the olden days (Charles I's time, which was

already History) all parts in all plays were played by men. Charles II had come over all modern in Europe and decided this was very old fashioned and that Britons should be more forward-thinking and have actresses. And so he did.

The most famous actress was Nell Gwyn, who had started off as an orange juggler and was later honoured with the title of Royal Mattress. Nell Gwyn had a child by Charles II who was a little bastard. In fact Charles II had many children by his many royal mattresses and even though they were all little bastards they went on to form the Backbone of the House of Lords as we know it, which just goes to show.

Another famous Stuart was Samuel Peeps. Samuel Peeps worked in the Government so saw everything that was going on and wrote it all down, as well as everything he did, in his diary. Mrs Peeps was also quite curious so Samuel wrote his diary in code so that she wouldn't know who he had been doing. Luckily for us Peeps was witness to two of the most exciting and Great Parts of History: The Great Plague of 1665 and the Great Fire of London.

The Great Plague

Still no one really knows where the plague came from or where it went to afterwards, but it certainly was in London in 1665. At first no one took much notice as it was only killing poor and dirty people who would probably have died of something else anyway. But then when rich people started getting it, everyone woke up and smelt the roses and panicked.

Everyone wanted to leave London, but weren't allowed in case they spread the plague all over the country. So Charles II and the courtiers all got out of the city and then locked the gates and went to Oxford. This did not go down well with Londoners, who felt abandoned and also, most of them, quite ill. If you had plague in your house they painted a red cross on the door and nailed it up so you couldn't get out and plague other people. So many people died that they had to dig huge holes for all the bodies, mostly under railway stations.

How you knew if you had the plague:

(1) you sneezed;

(2)   you had tokens (e.g. finding posies in your pockets);

(3)   you felt very ill;

(4)   you danced in a circle;

(5)   you fell down.

One story of Britons being Great during the plague happened in a village called Eyam. There was no plague in the village until some material arrived with germs in it and killed the village tailor. People were afraid and wanted to leave the village but the vicar called them all together and said they would only spread plague if they left, so he held them all at gunpoint until the plague was over. By the time the plague was over, most of them had died – but at least the vicar hadn't had to shoot anybody.

The plague was nearly over in London, and Charles II and the courtiers came back and unlocked the gates and everyone pretended not to notice that they had been abandoned, so as not to hurt the Merry Monarch's feelings.

The Great Fire of London

One night a London baker forgot to shut his oven door before he went to bed. When he got up the next morning, he was highly embarrassed to find that the whole of London, which was entirely whole-timbered, had utterly burnt down.

The Great Rebuilding of London

After the Plague and the Fire, everyone in London sat down and had a good think about how to make the new London better than the old one. Then, they did. They made there be rules about how tall, wide and far apart everything should be. Nothing was to be timbered any more; it all had to be made of bricks and mortarboards. They appointed the architect, Sir Christopher Robin, to build new churches – the best of these was St Paul's Cathedral, which continues to be famous for its Ethereal Dome and its Whispering Gallantry.

(Fascinating facts: Clapping your hands in the Gallantry produces four echoes. Accidentally tipping someone's packed lunch over the safety rail gets you thrown out.)

James I–V

There were five King Jameses and their lives were depressingly unfamiliar. Typically they were little boys when their fathers (the James before them) died, before he had had time to tell them whether he was King of Scotland or England or Both. (No one knows who the King of Wales was but perhaps, like Ireland, it hadn't been discovered yet. Remember the old sore: When the past is in another country, check that country exists first.)

This meant all the King Jameses spent a lot of time fighting wars trying to find out what they were King of. When they went to Scotland, the Scots would tell them they were only King of England, and when they went to England everyone said they were only King of Scotland. It was impossible to find out who was telling the truth, if anyone, but interestingly it never seems to have occurred to any of the Jameses that perhaps they were not really Kings of anywhere.

Samuel Stewart (aged 9)

(Nowadays reigning monarchs have to write down everything they are in charge of, so that if they die the next one knows and there's no messing about.)

James I is known for being so confused that he fled to France, earning him the nickname The Flying Scotsman. James II fled to Holland, earning him the nickname The Flying Scotsman II. James III, IV and V all married French Queens who made them stay at home (wherever that was).

Due to the lack of any firm information about what the Jameses might be kings of, Briton was ruled in the meantime by King Jacobin and Queen Caroline, about whom so little is known one could easily believe they never existed at all!

william and Mary

After King Jacobin and Queen Caroline died, the Britons had to quickly get new monarchs before one of the Jameses realised there was a vacancy, so got mail order ones from Holland. William of Orange turned out to be a bit of a Lemon, especially towards his wife, Mary, who was actually his cousin, but they didn't find this out until it was Too Late. Mary was a reluctant bride as she was taller than William and could see all his shortcomings.

William and Mary had a Glorious Revelation and realised that in order for Briton to get more Modern they should give more power to Parliament and end the tradition of Royal Prerogative (this means a monarch's right to change a woman's mind). Monarchs would no longer be autocratic and would instead do everything manually. There were huge festivities to celebrate, gallons of burgundy and clarity were consumed to produce a new royal dynasty:

the House of Hangover, which we still cherish to this very day.

William and Mary were never forgotten, partly because of making Monarchy More Modern, but mainly because of their enormous legacy to the development of Furniture. Both William and Mary had unusual legs (probably because they were cousins). William's had been fashioned while being spun on a lathe, while Mary suffered from what are variously termed ball, bun, hoof or turnip feet. Everyone now wanted tables and cabinets with these sort of legs and feet on, and also for chairs like Mary: thin with a high back and lavish embellishments.

Mary died of smallpox and William died of complications. (He fell off his horse when the horse tripped over a molehill, and his enemies began a tradition of toasting moles, saying 'Here's to the little gentlemen in black velvet waistcoats', before eating them.)

Queen Anne

Queen Anne, amazingly, managed to have 17 pregnancies in 17 years by 17 different fathers. If that wasn't enough of an achievement, she also united Scotland and England in a single sovereign state, for which neither country has ever forgiven her.

Being the late Queen Mary's sister, Queen Anne had inherited the family features, especially in the furniture legacy. She was smaller, lighter and more comfortable than Mary, having a cushioned seat and cabriole legs. Unfortunately, she became quite lame in later life, suffering from Scrolls On The Knees and beset by attacks of Urn-Shaped Splats. Anne's physical features went on to be lovingly recreated by craftsmen all over the country, so that long after her death her subjects were reminded of her every time they sat down.

The Georgians

The main thing to remember about the Georgian period is that everyone was mainly drunk most of the time. People committed crimes when they were drunk and then drunk judges sentenced them and drunk hangmen hanged them. It was all one big party.

Unfortunately, it was not all beer and roses. For example, wet-nurses didn't look after babies very well (being drunk at the time), often accidentally throwing them out with the bathwater, etc., losing them until they were found by a kind person (these children are called foundlings), losing them again (these children are called lostlings and it's the worst kind of child to be) and not being able to remember any of it in the morning, but only having a vague sense of unease and the phone hadn't been invented yet so they couldn't even ring round their friends and ask what they'd done, like Mum can.

The only saving grace is that the babies were probably also drunk as the drunk nurses gave them gin or opium to keep them quiet. So, in a way, they were lucky babies as they didn't know any better.

'Why did people drink so much?' I hear you cry. Some suggestions from historians:

(1) The water was so impure it was safer to drink anything other than water.

(2) The working classes were not dealing very well with 'enclosures' (see below) and other modern inventions like steam and machines and just thought they might as well drink their heads off as they could never earn enough to keep themselves, and what's the point? (Touch of the Middle Agers here, possibly.)

(3) Everyone just thought drinking was a Great Georgian Invention and did it all the time to be patriotic and support the economy and because it was Great.

This has all amply been caricterised and chara-catured by artists such as Gill Ray and Hogwart who did loads of pictures showing rich people behaving badly, but, much worse, poor people behaving badly, as poor people, as we know, are always expected to behave better than rich people. Hogwart's Rake's Progress showed just how much trouble could be caused with a simple garden tool, if the flesh was willing.

Georgians invented: fans, wigs, fops, lice, Luddites, slavery, etiquette, child labour, pirates, canals, Bath, enclosures, Brighton, quacking doctors, *beau brummels* (a sort of tight trouser) and roller skates or bow street runners.

George I (the first Georgian) was utterly incomprehensible to most British people, but surprisingly this was not because he was drunk (though doubtless, he was) but because he was German! This was a surprise to everyone, but they were very polite and British about it and pretended (a) not to notice and (b) to understand him. This led to some confusion but added to the mystique of royalty as no one has ever really been able to understand them ever since. For example, I bet you didn't know that our own Queen (Elizabeth II) is married to a Greek! Again, everyone has been very British about this and again pretended (a) not to notice and (b) to understand him.

This tolerance of difference and love of Johnnie Foreigner is all part of what makes Briton Great, even when Prince Philip is often clearly quite surprised about other foreigners and makes *faux pas*. This is Greek for 'slitty eyes' and is the face he pulls when he meets new ethical people, but everyone puts up with him because he is so old, and, due to his position as Queen's husband (but Not King, let's remember), commands universal disrespect of the highest order.

Anyway, back at History: George I died, and not one person knows anything about what George II did, so maybe he was completely German and no one ever understood, but he too died leaving the way for their youngest brother, George III, to rule for 60 extremely long and often insane years.

But before we get onto George III, let's remember we had a Parliament by now so there had been some Prime Ministers who should not pass muster. There was Sir Robert Walpole who was corrupt (let's remember the saying: 'Power corrupts. Absolute Power corrupts Absolutely Fabulously!') and Lord North who was mostly asleep, but the best one was William Pitt, who when he was Younger became Prime Minister at the tendentious age of 24 and when he was Elder carried on being decent and honest, though not about his age.

There were also some great Georgians who were neither Kings nor Prime Ministers and they were mainly Dick Turnip. Dick Turnip was a famous highwayman who has most erroneously gone down in History§ as a kind of Robin Cook (wanting to rob the rich to give to the poor, etc.) but, in fact, he was quite content with robbing the rich and giving it all, in his will, to his famous and faithful steed, Black Beauty. Black Beauty was famous for carrying Dick Turnip a very long way very quickly, and it is down to humans to remember her, as if you ask any horse whether they do, they always say 'nay' which is horse and old-fashioned language for: 'slightly good, but overrated in my opinion'. (Horses are like that, Great Grandma says, and there are plenty of them flying around her bedroom at the Home at night asking complicated questions about wool.)

One of the very annoying things that happened in Georgian times was Enclosures. Before Enclosures, every ordinary person (pheasant) had a little field they could grow stuff on, as well as working for the Lord of the Manner. (I would here like to take issue with Chardonnay's wording in her own account: 'Every pheasant had a little field they could grow shit on, as well as working for the Lord of the Manner, and shit like that'. I think Historians have to have standards, and I, at least, would like to pinhole them.) So they got a bit of money from him and a bit of money from how they cultivated themselves. 'Enclosures' meant that the Lord of the Manner could grab all the common land for himself and they couldn't have a vegetable plot any more, yet alone get more cultivated. This made them quite annoyed, and (probably being quite drunk as well, as it was traditional by now) they decided to have a massacre at Peterloo. The massacre didn't work out too well, as lots of the ordinary people got massacred, which was never the plan. Briton wisely decided, after this, never to have another massacre at home, but only to have them abroad. (One of the things I have noticed, having studied Briton's History quite introspectively, is that Briton, for all its faults, does Learn In The End, and only repeats its mistakes about three times.)

People were quite rightly cross because the price of corn was so high. It was elevated so far that most people couldn't even see it. But there was something else making them really cross and that was Slavery. For a long time British people had been working the land for no recompense, and they could never get out of debt, and the landowners ruled every area of their lives and they could never escape or better themselves, and now they saw poor people who were Africans had been putting up with it as well. That made them even more vexatious, because this was so rude and impolite to visitors (and part of what makes Briton Great is being hospitable to visitors and especially not flaying or shackling them or selling their children – that is considered very rude indeed) and they demanded that the black slaves be Set Free. Amazingly, the black slaves *were* set free, but the white pheasants were not and were still Enclosed. No one seems to have noticed this strange anemone.

Meanwhile, back at Main History...

In 1770, George III started feeling he didn't have enough Empire so he sent Captain Hook to go and get Australia to be part of it. The aborigines didn't understand what Captain Hook was saying when he asked them if they would like to be part of the Empire and just nodded politely like you do when Maninder's Grandma talks to you in Punjabi while pinching your cheeks quite hard, actually, so he took that as a 'yes' and went back and told the King. The King asked whether there were many people in Australia, and Hook had to go all the way back and count them and came back again and said, 'no, not really that many', and the King asked if it was far away enough that no one would be able to swim from Australia to Briton, and Hook said it definitely was too far and the King said: 'Good, because I want to send all our convicts there because our prisons here are full up.' Ever since that time, countries have got rid of people they didn't have room for by sending them to Australia and now Australia is quite Full and the Aborigines are still misunderestimated.

It is sometimes necessary to jump forward in History to tell a story that won't fit in anywhere else however hard you try, so I will add here that the white European settlers continued to behave very impolitely to the Aborigines, especially when they realised the Aborigines hadn't even invented the wheel yet. (This led to a spate of 'wheel' jokes which are now banned as Indiscriminating.) Also, once the Empire started happening in Australia all males had to be called Bruce and all women had to be called Sheila and the Aborigines didn't agree with this as they had had lots of lovely different names for people they had been using for years, like Blue Cockatoo and River, and no harm done. So the white people thought they had better make them see sense and began to 'rescue' Aboriginal children and make them more like white people. So they kidnapped them and called them Bruce and Sheila and put them in proper clothes and made them speak English and become alcoholics. (This is called 'assimilation' and it's what you do when you want to make everything similar to you rather than respecting Cultural Diffidence.) This didn't completely work, as the Aborigines still had their Art and their Music and their Culture which just kept coming back, like a boomerang when you are least expecting it, and now the white people have just given up and let the Aborigines have a bit of what is theirs back and hope they don't notice the very large bits of Australia that are now covered in wheels the Aborigines never needed in the first place. This is known as Multiculturalism, and you have it when your own culture doesn't deserve to win outright, only mainly.

(It was actually a good job Australia joined the Empire as America began to leave it at the same time, so it evened out, thus making it Fair.)

At the same time, the French Revelation was happening. The French people suddenly realised that King Louis XVI (the French were also still counting in Latin, which was helpful) and Queens Marie and Toinette were not looking after them as well as they should and they were definitely not getting enough cake. Even though in the end Marie and Toinette said they *could* have some cake, since it seemed to mean so much to them, it was too late and before you could say 'knife' the pheasants had chopped off their heads. Then the pheasants went through the French aristocracy, cutting everyone's heads off, and when they had run out of those they went for people who had, say, an aristocratic nose, or a haughty look, or even a bit of a posh voice. All the chopping off of heads actually got a bit tedious after a bit, and a group of women called the *tricoleurs* sat beside the guillotine knitting the new revolutionary flags to make it less boring and more colourful.

'Why do we need to know about the French Revelation when most of History is in Briton?' I hear you cry. 'Because', you hear me cry back, 'their new leader Neapolitan Bonaparte decided to have a war with Briton!' Even though he was foreign and therefore our enemy, Neapolitan was quite a character. Because he was a Brilliant Military Strategist he managed to make the war last 20 years. However he had not reckoned on Briton's Admirable Lord Horatio Nelson who beat him at the Battle of Trafalgar.

Though Nelson was a wily old sea dog he had already lost an eye and an arm in other battles and in this battle he did not see a cannonball coming and was fatally killed while he was busy kissing Hardy. Briton loved Nelson so much that they named a London square after him (useful, because before it had a name people must have had trouble finding it) and put a statue of him in it, very high up where no one could see it, so you just have to look at the lions instead and the Fourth Plinth where, excitably, anything happens, and you must not climb on it or feed the pigeons or you have to sit in the coach and 'think about what you have done' while the rest of the class goes to Buckingham Palace.

Eventually Neapolitan was caught and put on a desert island (Elbow), but everyone had demystifyingly forgotten about him being a Brilliant Military Strategist and he easily escaped and went back and fought the British again, this time at Waterloo. Again, he had not reckoned on the Duke of Wellington (leading the British) who outwitted him by having Prussians as well. Briton loved Wellington a lot too, but not as much as Nelson, so they only named a London railway station after his famous victory, and he didn't get a column or lions (or even pigeons). However, his name lived on anyway as The Duke of Wellington famously went on to invent the sandwich and the Big Band Sound, while Neapolitan was sent to live on another desert island (Saint Helena Bonham-Carter) and didn't escape and eventually died due to an absence of palindromes.

All in one King's reign Briton was in a war with France for 20 years (bad) and lost America (bad) and gained Australia (bad). How did this happen? What no one seems to have noticed is that George III was mostly mad a lot of the time and this explains a lot. Howsoever, Every Cloud has a Sliver of Lining, and this one was no exception. Due to George III being mad a lot of the time, he was mainly not in charge of Poetry, and this allowed some poets to invent being Romantic.

The main ones were Samuel Coleridge Taylor (also a composer) and William Wordsmith, but there were also others, including Percy 'Pish' Shelley, Lord Byron, Childe Harold, John F Keats, and, to a lesser intent, Charles Lambikins. Romantic Poets had rules about being one. Mainly, you had to write about Nature and, if possible, come to a Bad End. It was also an advantage if you had a clever sister to help you, although Byron misunderstood this and as a consequence ended up being 'bad, sad and injurous to know'.

While we are thinking about literature, it may be as well to mention Jane Austere, as everyone seems to think she was So Great. Jane Austere is famous for using the same plot several times and no one noticing. She also started a trend for Empire-line dresses and baths and Janeites, who are people who still haven't got over her. In some people's view she episiotomised women in Regency Society, and no one wants to see that.

Every time George III went a bit mad, his son (the Prince Regent) tried to get to be King With Indecent Haste and Alacrity. No one liked this, especially the Alacrity, which means 'wishing your dad is dead/officially declared permanently mad so you can be king properly'. But everyone put up with him because he would be King one day and then how would they look, etc. So everyone let him behave badly, have royal mattresses, build pavilions (mainly in Brighton), etc. until he was really King when poor old George III finally did go so mad he died of it.

Before then, George IV (the New King Formerly Known As Prince) had been allowed to pretend to be King when his dad was mad, and this is called being Prince Regent (reigning, but not really King). Once he was King properly, he became even better at doing nothing useful and being fat. He managed this for 10 years and then died, fortunately just at the moment that William IV was ready to take over.

Like George II, no one could remember anything about William IV's reign, but this was probably because they were mostly drunk. One day they all woke up with headaches and found the Victorian Age had begun without them.

The Industrious Revolution

No one worked harder than the Victorians, so they won easily.

The Victorians

The Victorians invented crinolines, poverty, spats, steam, novels, hackney-cabs, piano legs, London Peculiars, stays, orphans, and vestibules. They also discovered the rest of the British Empire, mainly in India and Africa.

(Most of the Victorian Age happened in London, although it was still quite Victorian everywhere else.)

SPECIAL SUMMER HOLIDAY PROJECT: PROMINENT VICTORIANS

Queen Victoria

Perhaps the Greatest Victorian of all was Queen Victoria, who accidentally married a German,

Prince Albert, but discovered this mistake only after they had had about twenty children and it was too late. As a result England and Germany had to be friends and unlikely bedfellows. All Victoria's and Albert's children went on to be kings and queens of all the other countries in the world, but sadly this did not prevent wars between them, which must have made Christmases a bit uncomfortable.

Dr Livingstone I. Presume

There were a number of Great Victorian Explorers, who went all over the world actually painting the towns red as we can see from old maps of the British Empire. The best Victorian explorer was Dr Livingstone I. Presume, who discovered Africa, got lost and was found by Stanley.

Stanley wrote a famous account of their meeting: as he walked into the camp where Livingstone was all the Africans were so excited at the arrival of the stranger that the men all banged drums while the women ovulated loudly. As the two Great Victorians approached each other, the

immortal words were uttered: 'Another fine mess you've gotten me into, Stanley.' This is because Livingstone I. Presume claimed he wasn't lost at all and knew perfectly well where he was, but Stanley insisted on discovering him just the same, and Livingstone had to go back to England to his angry wife.

Sir Shylock Holmes

We probably wouldn't know much about Sir Shylock Holmes except that his friend and assistant, Dr Watson, wrote it all down and published his stories in a magazine in the Strand.

Sir Shylock Holmes was a famous Victorian detective with an uncanny ability to work out who someone was or what they had been doing. (Mrs Cooper can do this too, to a lesser intent, and even when her back is turned can tell who threw Chardonnay's pencil case on the floor, while yanking her ponytail at the same time so hard she whelps in pain. 'I have Eyes In The Back Of My Head, Angus,' she says and keeps on pinning up the colours of the rainbow. It's quite demystifying.)

Howsoever, I have thought about this in just the way Holmes would – pushing the envelope outside the box. There are three highly suspicious things no historian seems to have noticed (and interestingly, no historian seems to take much notice of Sir Holmes at all). They are:

(1) Sir Shylock Holmes had a housekeeper, Mrs

Hudson, who used to collect visitors at the front door and then take them upstairs to Holmes's flat. It seems quite likely that they would have the usual chat during this time, e.g:

Mrs Hudson: Hello, and who might you be?

Visitor: I am recently widowed but not that sorry about it actually; I have two Persian cats and a verruca on my left foot which is causing some discomfort.

Mrs Hudson: I'm sorry to hear that, missus. More please.

Visitor: The slight twang in my accent is due to me being born in France but living in Australia until the age of three before coming to London to live with my mysterious benefactor.

Mrs Hudson: And the ink stain on the third finger of your right hand?

Visitor: Oh, that's just ink.

By this time they could have reached Holmes' door and Mrs Hudson could quite easily have filled Shylock in on the particulars while Dr Watson treated the visitor to palpitations.

(2) Shylock Holmes lived in Baker Street which is near the Marylebone Road which is where Madame Tussaud's is (because of the incident with Chardonnay and the cold pigeons and the small fire to keep them warm and Mrs Cooper making me also unfairly stay on the coach again when I was only helping, I do know the geography) where there was a lifelike model of nearly everyone in Victorian London (photography was then still taking a long time to develop). He could quite easily have recognised a lot of people simply by seeing the waxworks of them in his lunch hour and then just pretended to work it all out by himself.

(3) Whenever Shylock didn't know the answer to a question, he would just say: 'A lemon tree, my dear Watson.' This demystified Watson so much that Shylock could quickly change the subject without him noticing.

So Sir Shylock Holmes was probably not all he was cracked up to be. Mrs Hudson was later immoralised in an old-fashioned TV series called 'Upstairs, Downton' where she was the Cook and wife of the Butler, Mr Hudson. According to the Living Memory of Grandma, her part was mainly tutting a lot and just saying people's names in various ways, e.g: 'Oh, Mr 'Udson!' (shocked), 'Oh, *Rose...*' (disapproving), 'Oh, Milady!' (dishevelled), etc. while making food on a big table which no one ever ate. A sad end for Shylock's unsung heroin.

Jack the Ripper

Jack the Ripper was a very famous Victorian indeed, especially considering that no one ever knew who he was. People were always falling over in Victorian London, on account of the smog, bad pavements and horse poo everywhere. Men could easily get up again, but if a woman wearing a crinoline (see Victorian inventions) fell over, like a turtle she would find it very hard to get up again without help. (This was one reason why women weren't usually allowed out on their own.) Jack the Ripper used to look out for Fallen Women and then do indescribably lawful things to them while mutilating their reputations. This led to a widespread fear of becoming a Fallen Woman, so most women stayed indoors and had Vapours instead.

Charles Dickens

Charles Dickens was so famous that part of London was called Dickensian London. Unfortunately it was the worst part, where many of the Victorians' less good inventions were kept – e.g. smog, urchins, gin, pickpockets, winkles, cholera, street cries, mudlarks, porn shops, jellied eels, prisons, old inferiority shops, cockneys and gruel. However, everyone in Dickensian (bad) London had a Mutual

Friend in Victorian (good) London, and, bless my buttonhooks if, by a series of extraordinary coincidences, everything didn't come right in the end. Charles Dickens himself had been a poor boy and ended up a rich man, but never turned his back on his past, only on his wife. Dickens also invented Christmas where everyone ate and drank and made merry and said 'God bless us every one – except Tiny Tim!' and then laughed heartlessly before playing traditional games like Costermonger's Knock and Pass The Orphan.

Dr Barnardo

Contrary to popular disbelief, Dr Barnardo was not a real person, but a character invented by mischievous Charles (What The) Dickens. This loveable old missionary (principal character in The Missionary of Edwin Droop) went to London and was thunderstruck to see small children (or little dorrits, pickwicks or chuzzlewits, as he affectionately and variously named them) actually sleeping in the streets and totally begging for food and utterly without means to support themselves; in other words: prostitute.

In those days poverty was seen as the paupers' Own Fault, and probably the result of a Life of Laziness and Vice (like Lice, but more itchy). Dr Barnardo immediately set up a Rugged School where the children could go and get tough enough to survive this Life. He aimed to help children who were (a) bused, (a) bandoned (f) orgotten and (v) ulnerable. And he did! In the story by Dickens he soon had set up special Homes where children could go instead of being lostlings. The Boys' Homes taught them Trades and Crafts (like people do in the Third World now while we do Services, which are much More Modern and Insubstantial) and the Girls' Homes taught them Domestic Service (washing, ironing, cooking, cleaning and general incivility). Then when they were about six years old the boys could go and be chimney sweeps or work down the mines and the girls could be servile or do dumb insolence (like a dumb waiter but more satisfying) in someone else's house.

The moral of the story in which Dr Barnardo is a quite important character is Very Modern. Instead of taking babies away from Unmarried Mothers, he put them in a Nursery and found the Mothers jobs, and they could see their babies anytime they liked when they were not working their fingers to the bone, like today.

The babies grew up to be well-unbalanced individuals as a result of his intervention in their underdevelopment. Though Dr Barnardo remains a colourful character in some folks' history, he was entirely a pigment of Charles Dickens' imagination.

Infamous Victorian women

Florence Nightingale and Mary Seacoal

Both these women were among the first proper nurses. One was white and one was black and there the similarity ended. Florence Nightingale has been famous for a lot longer than Mary Seacoal. She was known as the Lady With The Lamp because she would go round the wards at night, waking all the soldiers up by shining the lamp in their faces, to see if they wanted anything to help them sleep, and then singing like a nightingale at them to tell them it was time to wake up again. This was during the Crimean War when no one knew anything about hygiene, and by simply leaving all the windows open so the soldiers could have fresh air, she managed to kill only half of them. Mary Seacoal did roughly the same, but while being black, which was harder.

Mrs Samuel Beetroot

Just like every home today has a cooking book by Jamie or Delia or Nigella, in the old days, no home was without a Mrs Samuel Beetroot. Mrs Beetroot's books on cooking basically saved the Victorians from starving to death. Unlike great-Grandma's recipes, written in her own hand, but not in French, 'thank the Good Lord,' as Mum says, which start: 'Take a dead chicken. Rub her all over with butter. Do not forget to cherish her under her legs, etc.' and continue in a mournful vain, Mrs Beetroot's recipes were jolly and mainly full of syllabub.

Her very tall husband, whose name she had to have, it being Those Days, was a Giant in Publishing, and chose, when she died, to keep her Name Alive, as he loved her so much, and brought out loads more books apparently written by Her, from Beyond The Grave. Thus we can see that the old maxim is true: it is better to have cooked and died than never to have lied at all.

Isabel Kingdom of Brunel

Despite being handicapped from an early age by being a girl, Isabel cunningly dressed as a man and so was able to become a Prominent Victorian Engineer. She built:

(1) massive bridges;

(2) massive ships;

(3) massive tunnels, including the first Channel Tunnel, which she abandoned when she realised it would end up in France.

Brunel loved iron (so much that she even had her hat made out of a stovepipe). This led to a new Iron Age, which was part of the Steam Age and eventually led to the Steam Iron, which we still have today, one of the many modern labour-saving devices which mean women can do housework AND go out to work at a proper job nowadays. This is called Doing It All and modern women are the first generation to Do It All which is why they are so much happier than previous generations.

The Brontës

The Brontës were a famous family of writers who lived (and probably sang) in close harmony. There was Charlotte, Emily, Anne and their brother Bramwell, the Bad Apple of the family. Charlotte, Emily and Anne were all Great Writers but only they knew this, and they did not tell their father or their brother, as then it wouldn't have been a secret, which it had to be, because if you were a woman in Those Days you couldn't be a writer, so they had to *pretend* to be men and *really be* writers to the outside world and only *be* women and *pretend not to be* writers at home. This often made them all ill and several earlier sisters died under the strain of it all.

This was a shame because they had had a brilliant childhood where their father let them burn furniture and eat nothing but potatoes if they liked. If they were very badly behaved, he simply sent them away to be governesses and when they came back they all had very good ideas for books. Bramwell was clearly confused by all this (he couldn't be a governess and get ideas) and went to the bad – drinking, taking drugs, falling in love with marred women and crashing trains and being a great worry to them all.

Eventually, everyone found out that the Brontë sisters were not men at all and were disgusted. Suddenly their books, which everyone had thought were Great, became Bad Books written by Bad Women. Bramwell locked them all in the attic and pretended they were dead and married Jane Eyre, who later discovered them and ran away because by now, they had all gone stark staring mad with being locked in the attic and not knowing who or what they were. The Brontë sisters then burned the house down and made new lives. Their reputations lay in tatters but their friend Mrs Gasket dropped in and repaired them all good as new so everyone would like the Brontës again, which they did. It was, of course, all far too late, because although Anne had stayed at home to look after their poor blind father, Emily had run away with the tenant of Wildfell Hall and poor Charlotte had died after a particularly severe attack of the Wuthering Heights.

No one even thought about the Brontës for about a hundred years until Kate Bush catapulted them back into the limelight using *just her voice* and thanks to her, their names will live on fraternally. An exact replica of their house stands in the sight of the original and if you go there you can see just how cramped it must have been (especially on a Bank Holiday).

Some Interesting Things About History

One interesting thing you need to know about History is that the closer it gets to Now the more of it there is. So there is a lot more history about the Victorians than, say, the Ancient Egyptians, because (a) it is nearer and less forgettable and (b) it is in English so people were writing it down in a way we could understand (remember the reliable axel: 'When the past is in another country it's often in another language', etc.).

History depends, to some extant, on Living Memory. This is when there is someone still alive who can actually remember what was going on that long ago. For example, my Great Grandad knows all about being an Evacuee, Rationing and how very Unpopular the King and Queen were when they visited the bombed-up East End of any city looking sad and well-fed (a Fact on which he and Mrs Cooper disagree). On the one *other* hand, my Great Grandma is literally Living in the Past, and can name everyone in her street when she was five years old but does not have a clue what day of the week it is or where she put her specs (in the microwave).

While Living Memory may seem a reliable source of History, it can be Unreliable. This is also known as False Memory. Some people think they were in the Holocaust when they were really just down the shops. A lot of people think they were Neapolitan or Cleopatra in a previous life (and quite a few of them are in Great Grandma's Home) but of course they can't all have been. It stands to reason.

So it's best to put Living Memory with all other History and take it with a pinch of salt and remember that people just fill in the gasps of what they can't remember.

Howevertheless, it's important to tell the difference between Primary Sauces (someone there at the time telling all about it) and Secondary Sauces (someone later saying what it all meant) and Tertiary Syphilis, which is utterly different, hard to understand and probably just Bad News.

Another important thing to know about History is that it is written by the Winners. Losers used not even to be allowed to write about History because of the Sour Grapes Factor. Like sour grapes, it makes everyone feel a bit sick when they read slaves or women telling their side of the story. History written by Losers is called Alternative History, which is a bit like Alternative Comedy but definitely not nearly as funny. When women write Alternative History it is called Herstory and I can tell you there are very few laughs per page there.

Feminininist History (as it is called) was mainly written in the 1970s (when, of course, History was still going on) and was very angry and Militant and the women cut their hair off and refused to wear make-up and wore dungarees and everyone had to Burn Their Bra because it was an Instrument of Oppression, also known as the Patriarchy.

This was followed by Post Feminininism when people were embarrassed to say they were Feminininists and only wrote letters about it. The embarrassment was on account of the Militarism, which the Feminininists had blamed on Men who had started all wars, etc. and they suddenly realised that their own Militantism was a Bad Thing and also when you go to the loo in dungarees everything falls out of the pockets, according to the Living Memory of my Grandma.

The Edwardians

Although there had been six King Edwards before, only Edward VII had an Age named after him. Although Edward VII also had potatoes and cigars named after him, he did not do much History – but he just let it happen, anyway. The main thing that he let happen was...

The Suffragettes

Like History, with a few expectations, Women did not really exist until the Suffragettes were invented. They were so called because they wanted men and women to have equal suffering, and eventually they got it, as we can see to this day. It is quite amazing to think that as long as History is (possibly 2,000 years) women were not properly allowed to be part of it until the last hundred. How did anything get done at all?

The answer is: they were there All The Time! They had just been shy and hiding in the kitchen.

When the Suffragettes came, they changed all that and freed the women (many of whom had been chained to their kitchen sinks) and made women go out into the street and shout and throw stones and sing while they were doing it. The Suffragettes also had a rule that whenever a suffragette saw the King on his horse they had to throw themselves under it. They were quite good at this but Emily Wildly Davison mistimed her stunt and got trampled. Because the Patriarchy got to write the History at the time they explained this by saying she was Mad so that was alright.

(The Winners often say the people against them are Mad or a Terrorist, but then when the Winners become Losers, it often turns out that the new Winners (ex-Losers) were quite Sane and Freedom Fighters – e.g. Horatio Nelson Mandela – and the new Losers (ex-Winners) were really the Mad ones. This is known as the Sanity Clause and you can find it all over History.)

The main suffragettes were the Parkhursts, a family/tribe who were so numerous the Patriarchy had to build a special prison to put them all in. While they were in prison the Suffragettes/Parkhursts decided that that was still not enough suffering so they all went on Hunger Strike. Then the Patriarchy realised that if any of the Parkhursts actually died of starvation the Patriarchy/Government/Bras would look very bad and get blamed by Pubic Opinion, so they invented the Cat and Flap Act. This meant that when a Suffragette got so ill she might die, they let her out (quietly, like a cat through a flap in the prison door) but as soon as she got better and looked like she was not going to die they snatched her back in through the flap again.

The Parkhursts would then start Hunger Striking all over again and the Patriarchy got so worried that it tried Force Feeding them. (If you have ever tried to give a hamster a tablet you will know how hard and painful and unpleasant this is and the hamster does not like it much either.) This did not work, as Pubic Opinion, which was beginning to agree with women having equal suffering with men, heard that this was happening to rich ladies as well as ordinary women, and certainly did not want them suffering equally.

In the end, the Suffragettes won, and then women could write History as well. All the horse -hurdling and hunger-striking had been worthwhile, in the name of Female Emaciation, which has continued to this day.

World War 1

The First World War wasn't originally called 'The First World War' because historians didn't think there would be another one. The First World War was so awful that everyone believed it must be The War To End All Wars, but unfortunately it was only the First of Two (so far). So, before anyone knew there would be a Second World War, the First World War was called The Great War.

However, it was not Great at all, quite the opposite. People at home in Briton continued to think the War was Great, while the poor soldiers fighting it in France and Belgium knew it was Not Great but Couldn't Talk About It.

(The Third World War will probably have to happen in the Third World – e.g. parts of Africa – or it could be a bit confusing. Hopefully it won't happen at all, but if there are any historians reading this they probably should start thinking about a new labelling system.)

How the Great War started in the first place is quite demystifying. Serbians shot Austria's next emperor in the balkans, which must have hurt like anything, but instead of Austria invading Bosnia or Serbia, due to some kind of mix-up Germany invaded Belgium and France. Before anyone had a chance to realise their mistake the so-called Great War had started and soon too many men had died for anyone to admit to the fact that it had all been an awful misunderestimation in the first place.

Everyone was very patriotic in those days so Briton was eager to get into the War too, and when a rumour got out that it would all be over by Christmas, lots of young men enthusiastically rushed off to become 'Tommies' and get killed before the deadline. If they didn't rush off to get killed quickly enough people would make them eat white feathers as a punishment for being a coward, or a pacifist. The speed with which soldiers got killed after arriving at the Front broke all records. When the soldiers got to the War and saw how it really wasn't Great at all, if they refused to join in, or ran away, their own army would shoot them just to save time.

One of the things that really didn't help matters was that there were a lot of animals on the battlefield. All the armies were still using Calvary, which is a way of crucifying horses by sending them into battle against machine guns and tanks. There are also unconfirmed reports that lions were used. This was quite a brilliant idea (if true), but unfortunately, the High Command, who were out of touch with the lions on the ground, ordered for them to be led by donkeys. That arrangement was clearly an accident waiting to happen, and it did.

The Great War had a few main problems. They were:

(1)   A lot of the War was fought in Flander's Fields. No one knows who Flander was, but his Fields were extremely muddy, and everything sank in them, making both Advancing and Retreating very difficult, so everyone stayed where they were, waiting for Christmas.

(2)   In the middle of Flander's Fields was a bit of land that wasn't Flander's, but no one knew who

it belonged to, so it was called No Man's Land.
This is the bit that the French and British Versus
the Germans were fighting over.

(3) Christmas came, and the War was still
clearly determined to go on, whether the
Germans and British wanted it to or not. It had
gained a memento all of its own, which can still
be seen on every village green in Briton.

The best thing that could happen to a soldier
was to Cop-A-Blimey-One. This meant they
got an injury which was not bad enough to kill
them, and not good enough to keep them at the
Front, but a medium one that meant they had
to be sent back to Good Old Blighty (or Briton)
to get well enough to come back and be killed
later. Tommies would say 'Blimey!' to express
their great good luck when this happened.

As well as injuries, soldiers had to confess
with Rats, Lice and French Foot. French Foot
was a disease the French had accidentally left
in some trenches and made your boots smell
like someone had peed in them. The trenches
were quite dirty and quite wet and quite full of
bits of poor blown up soldiers. Rats liked this

environment and Lice did not so the Lice lived on the soldiers, who were drier. While this was all very nice for the Rats and Lice, it was not so good for the soldiers and what with being bombed all the time as well, some of them got a bit depressed and had Shell Shock. This happened when a Tommy suddenly realised the War was Pointless and that Nearly Everyone on both sides was going to Die before it would end, and was so shocked he went a bit mad. Sometimes he would go so mad he went right Over The Top and if this didn't kill him he might be lucky enough to Cop-A-Blimey-One (see above).

As previously understated, the soldiers couldn't Talk About The War, but they could Write About It. They were not allowed to write letters home telling their families how terrible and wrong the War was, but only good things about the War, so no one wrote any letters at all. This probably meant that when the soldiers who hadn't been killed (probably about a hundred) went home, exhausted and shocked, after four years of fighting all they got was a massive telling-off from their mums.

They could write poetry though as High Command had forgotten to make a law against that. They would go about the battlefield collecting similes and metatarsals and put them in poems. The Great War produced some Great Poets, such as Wilfred Oven, Siegfried Bassoon and Rupert Book. Robert War Graves also wrote a funny book called 'Goodbye to 1914-18 and All That'. Writers believe that The Pen Is Mightier Than The Sword. Unfortunately, the War Poets had not caught up with the times and discovered it is not mightier than shells and machine guns so lots of them got killed advancing on the enemy armed only with sharpened pencils.

Both sides were told how utterly awful the other side was and tried to believe in it. The British called the Germans The Bosh or The Hun, which are quite rude words in German, and believed they ate babies. The Bosh or Hun believed the British Tommies ate horses, which they probably did, actually. (As usual the British and Germans were having their war in someone else's country – usually France or Belgium – as absolutely everyone believed the French ate frogs.)

However, one cold and snowy Christmas when

the soldiers were all beginning to wonder whether they had misheard in the first place and whether they had in fact been told 'The War will all be over by [an unspecified] Christmas [in a few years' time]', the Tommies in their trenches were missing their mums, etc. and heard the Huns in their trenches on the other side of No Man's Land singing a Christmas carol and it occurred to them that maybe the Huns were, after all, just German Tommies. Then an extraordinary thing happened...

1st Tommy: (calling out of trench) Oi! Fritz! Merry Christmas! (He throws a packet of biscuits over No-Man's Land into the German trench.)

1st Hun: (calling out of trench) Gott und Himmel! Thank you Tommies! Merry Christmas to you too! (He throws a dud shell back for a joke.)

2nd Tommy: (after a short break of great alarm) Shall we *not* fight today and play football instead? As it's Christmas?

2nd Hun: Donner und Blitzen und Prancer und Vixen! Excellent idea, Tommies.

And then all the Huns and all the Tommies came slowly out of their trenches, both worried that it might be an impractical joke, and the closer they got to each other the more they realised they were just the same (but obviously still German and British). They put their guns down and went and shook hands. From then on it went from bad to better and everyone made friends before playing a gentlemanly game of football. Everybody was having a lovely time – especially the British who were winning 2-0 – when a German goal was declared offside.

And then one of the Huns named *all eight* of Rudolph the Red-Nosed Reindeer's companions (which is as angry as a German can actually get at Christmas) and everything looked a bit dodgy for a moment and·there was a freezing silence. Then...

3rd Tommy: (breaking the ice with a joke all the soldiers would appreciate) Let's do *Somme* thing else.

All the soldiers laughed till they cried. They quickly made friends again and showed each other pictures of their sweetbreads.

Then they gave each other guided tours of their horrible homes in the trenches. And when the

Tommies looked in the German trenches and saw they bought their concrete from the very same company as they did, they felt awful. And when the Germans looked in the British trenches and saw the English cooking the Tommies had had to eat, they felt terrible. So the Tommies gave the Germans cigarettes (smoking was still good for you in those days) and the Germans gave the English sausages and ham and chocolate and sauerkraut and cinnamon buns.

It was getting dark by now and was time to go home. The Germans thanked the Tommies for not giving them any British food and the Tommies thanked the Germans for their warm hostility and all the soldiers sadly returned to their own trenches with mixed failings. And the next day, they all got on with killing each other again.

When the War finally ended, everyone was very relieved and no one at home really wanted to hear how awful and wrong it had been so the killing fields of Flander's were soon all covered over with poppycock.

George V

We are now onto the Modern Merry Monarchs and George V was the most Modern so far, although it took him quite a long time to realise this.

Due to Briton being a Marinaded Nation, George went to sea when he was 12 and didn't come back till he was a well-seasoned sailor of 27. To welcome him home Queen Victoria gave George (her grandson) his dead brother's fiancée, Mary, as a present. George was not good at expressing his feelings, so Mary encouraged him by sending him love letters containing terms of entrapment until he made her his wife.

George and Mary travelled wildly, visiting India, Canada, South Africa, Australasia and New Zealand (not to mention the Antipodes). His hobbies were Bloodsports and Philately: he loved killing animals and spent hours sticking his collection in stamp albums.

When the First World War started, George found himself in the embarrassing position of having lots of German relations (see Uncomfortable Christmases, under Victorians) – indeed, even the German Kaiser Chief was his cousin. He needed somehow to make these cousins distant ones without hurting their feelings. So, like when we moved house and Mum and Dad made sure they didn't give Auntie Sarah our new address and phone number, George changed his German surname without telling his cousins so they wouldn't be able to find him. He crossed out 'House of Saxa-Carlsberg-Gothic' and put 'Windsor' instead. He also ordered his female cousins to drop their territorial designations and never let them put them on again.

George also noticed that a lot of other countries were having Revelations, especially in Russia, where the Tsar happened to be another of his many cousins. He didn't want a Revelation happening in Briton so tried to make the Royal Family a bit more like normal people. He decided to stop being so Aloof and had relationships with Trade Unionists (much to Mary's unhappiness) and pretended to be interested in ordinary working people.

Old-style king George V opening a new car park: I declare this car park open.

Crowd: Hurrah!

New-style king George V opening a new car park: Hello, my fine fellow me lad, and what do you do?

Man: I'm a plumber, your worship.

George V: Really? What on earth is that?

Man: I fix drains and pipes and so on, your lordship.

George V: Really? What on earth are they? This all sounds very eyebrow. Do tell me more, you intriguing and endlessly fascinating little chap, etc. Oh, and I declare this car park open.

Crowd: HURRAH!

At Christmas in 1932, George V made his first Radio broadcast to the Nation, thus entering the heart of every home that had one. At first he resisted the exercise as self-indulgent, but it pleasured everyone so much that it became a popular manual event.

At George V's funeral, the crown fell off of

the coffin and landed in the gutter. The new King, Edward VIII (Edward the Cad), wondered whether it was a significant omen, as he was worried about reconstyling his own needs with his Duty To The Crown, and having Doubtful Miss Givings at the same time.

Edward VIII

George and Mary had had six children who were all boys except for a girl. George V still has an unreserved reputation as a very strict father, but this is not true, as the King said himself: 'My father was frightened of his mother, I was frightened of my father, and I am damned well going to see to it that my children frighten me.' The one that frightened him most was the eldest and heir to the throne, Edward. Edward dressed like a Cad and walked like a Bounder to keep up with the Fast Set. He also terrified his father by not being a sailor and having affairs with women instead.

The worst love affair was with Mrs Simkins. It was the worst because Edward wanted to actually marry her. Up until then, kings and queens got married to the cousin they disliked least and love was strongly discouraged, as you can fall out of love but you can't fall out of a cousin. There was No Way Mrs Simkins could be Queen as she was (a) American (b) A Divorcee (c) Wore fashionable clothes that didn't look like they'd belonged to the last Queen and the Queen before that etc.

While Mrs Simkins could have tried to be as dowdy as a dowager, she could not, of course, become UnAmerican or UnDivorced. (It is quite strange that everyone minded so much about her being divorced, as if she had still been married she couldn't have married Edward either: something many historians seem not to have noticed. As the old saying goes: When the past is in another country, if it's America it should probably stay there.)

His mother was telling him one thing and Mrs Simkins was telling him another. Edward was caught between two stooges: should he marry the woman he loved and Not Be King or should he be King and Give Up The Woman He Loved? Then someone thought of a third plausibility: he could not marry her *and* not be King. This is known as a Morganatic Solution, to make it instantly forgettable.

In any case, Edward did what no other King

has ever done and resigned before he was even crowned. This is called Abdicating Responsibility and you do it when you can't marry who you like and still be King, or when you refuse to attend Parents' Evening with your only son.

Ever since the Abdication Crisis the Royal Family have made sure they all marry people they don't like First, and then marry someone they like Second and try a bit harder this time. This is again evidence of:

- the Royal Family being just like normal people;

- the Great British Art of Compromise, shown in the saying 'If at first you don't succeed, try , try, and try again something completely different';

- the Royal Family's ability to respond to Pubic Opinion, and Move With The Times (or at least *The Guardian* or *The Independent*).

George VI

If you can imagine that everyone was quite annoyed when Edward VIII ended his reign before it began (having to cancel their street parties and make their families eat the gallons of Coronation Chicken they had already prepared for tea every day for a month), you can imagine how much more annoyed the next King was, as Edward's younger brother, who had never expected to have to be King, now had to very suddenly sit on the throne and remain there for some time until his daughter Elizabeth, who was then only little, needed to use the bathroom.

George VI (George The Good) turned out to be a Great King but had been cruelly beaten by his father (George V) when small, who hit him about the head repeatedly with a stammer, which had stuck. Some people were worried he wouldn't be a Good King and they were also worried about the – now traditional – Christmas Broadsides.

Fortunately, he was married to the Queen Mother, who knew exactly what to do. The Queen Mother was a National Treasure. These are very rare and are usually locked up in the Tower of London, but somehow she had managed to escape and now proved herself of culpable value. Basically, she taught all the Royal Family to cover up the King's stammering by smiling sweetly and changing the subject.

The Scene: George VI and the Queen Mother are launching a ship. (Fortunately they have brought a number of people to help them.)

George VI: I name this sh- sh- sh- sh-

Queen Mother: Isn't this simply shocking weather? Still, better than no weather at all, I say!

Crowd: Hurrah!

George: ...sh- sh- sh- sh-

Queen Mother (loudly): Hello, dear little man, and what do you do?

Man: I'm a riveter, milady.

Queen Mother: How enchanting. But what do you do, actually?

Man: I drive rivets into ships, milud.

George: ...sh- sh- sh- sh-

Queen Mother (louder): Isn't that frightfully dangerous? Do you have to have a licence? Have you come far? Do you have a family? I'll wager they're a credit to you, bless their little cottonsocks. What are the odds, do you think?

George: Ship!

Queen Mother (aside): Well done, darling.

Crowd: HURRAH!

George VI and the Queen Mother had two daughters. One was Elizabeth, who is of course our lovely juicy currant Queen, and the other was Margaret, who unfortunately was not allowed to marry the man she loved and consequently became extremely morganatic.

The main thing George VI and the Queen Mother did was See Everyone Through The War (the Second World One). They sent their little girls to be safe in Sandringham or Windsor or Balmoralglenbogle, but they stayed in London throughout the festivities, often getting bombed, strafed, or utterly trolleyed – mainly on Gin.

Eventually, George VI's stammer became too much and finally killed him. This ushered in the New Elizabethan Age, which is the beginning of Now, so History is finally catching up with itself.

But we now have to go back and catch up with a bit of George VI's reign, which didn't only reign but poured.

World War II

For quite a long time after The War To End All Wars, Germany had been thinking about how it could get even, and then cunningly thought that Another War would be just what no one was expecting, so they decided to sneakily start one. This was all made plausible by Adolf Heil Hitler.

Adolf Hitler, although Austrian, spoke German voraciously. Initially a popular comedian, lots of Germans repeated his jokes to each other and began to feel a lot better about losing the last war. He had a funny moustache and an entertaining comb-over ('Less a hairdo and more a hairdon't,' according to Dad, who should know) and many soldiers imitated his hilarious walk. Heil Hitler got everyone feeling that it was Great to be German again and everyone started to think that Germany should be Great again too and they got so carried away with this idea and enjoying themselves doing exercises, going to rallies and cabarets and singing 'Tomorrow Belongs To Me' that they didn't notice Hitler becoming very serious indeed. In fact, he was becoming quite a fascist.

Unfortunately, by the time Germans realised that some of Hitler's jokes weren't that funny and some weren't jokes at all, they had voted him into power and he had made himself Furious (or *Führer* in German). Then the trouble really started. This part of History is called the Holocaust and it is so horrible I am not even going to have it in my book.

Having a war not only distracted people from noticing the Holocaust was going on, but also meant Germany would get a lot bigger, as it had had bits confiscated after the last war and everyone was feeling a bit cramped. Hitler said they needed 'living space' (or *Lederhosen*) and proposed taking back the bits they'd lost and then quite a bit more, in fact, possibly the whole world.

First, Germany cleverly got invited to invade Austria, so it didn't look like a war, and then it decided to go and 'visit' Poland, but England, by now, had begun to wake up and see what was really going on and everyone in Briton gathered round the (probably about a hundred) radios that had so far been invented to hear what would happen next.

The British Chamberlain went to talk with the Germans and when he came back said: 'I hold in my hand a piece of paper,' and everyone was very relieved as they thought it was a peace treaty. But he had forgotten to check what was written on it, and it turned out that the cunning Germans had given him a blank piece of paper! Then the Chamberlain said on the radio that he had told Germany that if it 'visited' Poland it would have to supply all the undertakers to deal with all the dead soldiers, and then said solemnly that because 'no such undertakers had been received, we are At War With Germany'.

The Chamberlain then got the sack on account of not having even checked the piece treaty was real and Britain had a Coition (i.e. two parties joined together) Government led by the immoral Sir Winsome Churchill, but even though the Government was a Coition one, he was Prime Minister, as someone had to be. (No one can now

even remember who else was in the Government, so it was probably The Liberal Democrats.)

Sir Winsome Churchill was a Great Briton right from the start and together with his lovely wife Dame Vera Lynn kept the home fires burning in every major city throughout the war. Churchill liked fighting in the air and at sea and on land but, best of all, he liked fighting on the beaches (though not at Dunkirk, where great granddad says the British Tommies were throwing their guns away and saying 'What's the point? etc.' but Mrs Cooper again begs to differ here) but in fact, there was very little fighting on beaches until D-Day when the British finally decided to go to Europe themselves and sort it all out once and for all.

But before that there was quite a long time of Briton getting bombed by Germany and trying not to be invaded itself. It was an uneven conflict.

The Germans had:
(1)   Adolf Hitler as leader;
(2)   Superior air power;
(3)   Conquered nearly all of Europe.

The Britons had:
(1) Sir Winsome Churchill as leader;
(2) Plenty of things to melt down and make planes with (railings, nails, paperclips, etc.);
(3) Sea all around them.

One of the Germans' ingenious plans was to send bluebirds over the white cliffs of Dover, who reported back to Hitler on where all the big guns were kept. German spies also parachuted in at night, dressed as nuns, and would take down all the road signs, and paint everyone's headlights black, hoping that the British would keep getting lost and bumping into each other. This did not work as the British were all drinking Blitz Spirit to keep up morale. (Blitz Spirit was the only thing that wasn't rationed during the war, apart from sandbags, fish and chips and bunting.)

London was full of cheeky chirpy Cockneys who spent all day sliding down the roof of St Paul's Cathedral throwing off any incendiary ideas that had landed there, while singing songs, accompanied by someone thumping away on Old Joanna.

The countryside was full of Evacuees and POWs. Evacuees is a name for children from cities whose parents sent them to the country supposedly so the children would be safe from all the bombing, but probably the parents just wanted to read the paper, work in ammunitions factories, do Knees Up Mother Brown and get bombed in peace. POWs were Prisoners Of War: enemy soldiers who Briton (or someone) had captured in Europe and brought back to Briton as a punishment. They worked on farms, etc. as the farm-workers were away in the British army catching more POWs to do their jobs while they were away, which was quite clever, when you think about it.

One bit of the war was called The Battle For Briton. This was fought in the air between the RAF (British) and the Lufthansa (German). Although the Lufthansa technically had what Historians term 'superior air power' but is really 'more planes', the RAF won probably because their planes had better names (eg. Spitfire) which is good for morale.

Both sides had incendiary/fire bombs which were very terrible indeed and were used to stun Coventry (in Briton) and Dresden (in Germany). Dresden was famous for its blue-and-white china, and Coventry was famous for being the place you sent people (in the olden days) who no one wanted to talk to any more, so they were both clearly important targets.

Although Briton thought these were good bombs to drop on Germany, they did not like these bombs so much when they were dropped on Briton, so everyone now agrees (History being written by the Winners, etc.) these were Bad Bombs, as opposed to Good Bombs, such as the RAF's Bouncing Bombs which sounded more jolly and were much better than ordinary bombs and way more cool, as they could bounce along a river and break a dam which would flood a town, so people could be killed by one bomb instead of lots of bombs, which was much more modern.

As you will remember ('*if* you have been paying *attention*, Chardonnay,' as Mrs Cooper says), France and Briton had been enemies long ago but had been the best of friends since time war memorial. However now it all went a bit wrong. When Germany invaded France, it all happened a bit too easily for Briton's liking. Neapolitan had thoughtfully planted trees all along the French roads so the Germans could march in the shade, which seemed a bit suspicious for a start.

Then the French gave up half the country and said Germany needn't tramp all over it invading and getting its muddy boots all over it, and it could run itself thank you very much, but just how Germany wanted it to be run (*Vichyssoise* France) thereby saving everyone the trouble of bombing, etc. The other half of France still wanted to be Free, so the Germans had to come in and occupy it, act like they owned the place, tramp over everything, put up signs telling everyone what to do, etc. (see The Romans). These French started up a secret gang called, in towns, *La Resistance* (which means The Resistance) but in the countryside it was called *La Marquee* (which means The Marquee). They didn't manage to get rid of the Germans but they did slow them down with sabotage and long lunches.

However, the British had a secret weapon: America. They had used this secret weapon in the Great War, but the thing about this secret weapon was that it could only be used at the Last Minute as America didn't like going abroad and had always lost its passport and took ages to pack, etc. In those days, America only liked to go in a war when it knew it could win, which you can't really tell until quite near the end, so they would wait until it was all looking OK and then come along and join in so they would be in the photos at the end.

Eventually Churchill had the brilliant idea of invading Europe, which he thought was probably the last thing the Germans were expecting, and also meant he could finally have some fighting on the beaches.

The 1950s

After the war, Britons were all poor and tired and Briton itself was mainly homemade or in black-and-white. Lots of food was still rationed and that made everyone even more miserable and they couldn't even be bothered with making soup out of bunting anymore. They were so fed up that they didn't even let Sir Winsome Churchill carry on being Prime Minister and they elected an Old Labour government, on the basis that Things Can Only Get Better (which turned out to be true, actually, as by the 1960s They'd Never Had It So Good). Old Labour, like wine, was much better and more mature than New Labour, and even though it is in Living Memory most people have forgotten what it was like, so it's still in History. Let's remember what Old Labour said:

🖖 everyone can have a home;

🖖 everyone can have a job;

✋ everyone who can't get a job can have some money anyway;

✋ everyone can go to school free;

✋ everyone can go to the doctor's and dentist's free.

So, it's quite easy to see why people preferred it to Winsome making them all fight at the seaside and tighten their belts until the pipsqueaks fell out.

However, everyday life was still quite dreary and shabby and it rained for most of the 1950s until, as at the end of most World Wars, the Americans saved the day by sending two lots of relief: Glorious Technicolor and Rock and Roll! Now that everything was in colour life was much better for everyone, but unfortunately, Rock and Roll only cheered up the young people, and the old people didn't like it at all, mistaking it for an Infernal Racket (but it was really Rock and Roll) and this continued into...

The 1960s

The gap between old and young was widening till soon they could hardly hear each other think. The old people stood on one side shouting at the young ones to cut their hair, show some respect, turn that down, get a proper job, take their feet off the table, etc. and the young ones lounged about on the other side not listening, making daisy chains, playing guitars, Sticking It To The Man and smoking cannabis. (This was known as Pot Culture.) They did not believe in winter and replaced it with a Summer of Love which lasted for most of the sixties. However, it was not all bells and whistles, and mum says there were Untold Casualties of the Summer of Love – namely unmarried mothers having to have babies in L-shaped rooms or Up The Junction, and some young people who had taken too many drugs even went a bit psychedelic.

The 1970s

The 1970s are fondly remembered for the Winter of Discontent. There were a lot of strikes in this decade but at one point, by complete coincidence, absolutely everyone went on strike at the same time and the country ground to a halt. The trains didn't run, the rubbish didn't get collected, and the dead had to bury themselves. Even the Government was completely paralytic most of the time.

Gradually the Government started to get things going again, by introducing one day of work into the week at a time. By the time there was a Three Day Week people were pretty sure everything was going to be OK, but then they accidentally elected Mrs Margaret Thatcher to be Prime Minister. The whole of Briton was completely Decimalised.

The 1980s

Mrs Thatcher was known as The Iron Maiden because she had a heart made entirely of steel.

Things Mrs Thatcher abolished:

- free school milk;
- council houses;
- coal-miners;
- alternatives;
- U-turns;
- society;
- the Berlin Wall.

In 1981, The Archbishop of Canterbury married Prince Charles and Lady Diana. It appeared to be a match made in Harrods, but actually turned out to be Woolworths. It was doomed from the start because apparently there was a third person in the marriage and neither of them knew who it was (although it seems fairly obvious that it must have been the Archbishop of Canterbury). At the time, though, everyone was very happy about having a Royal Wedding and thousands of people came out on the streets of Brixton and Toxteth to celebrate round communal bonfires for several days. Even the Police joined in the fun.

Mrs Thatcher got a bit jealous about the attention Charles and Diana were getting so she decided to invent the Falkland Islands. The Falkland Islands had just been invaded by Argentina who had Lost Malvinas so wanted some new islands to make up for that. Anyway, Briton won, as usual, and didn't even invite the Americans to join in, for a change, perhaps because the Falklands are a bit nearer to America than to Europe and Americans understandably like their wars to be quite far away from where they live.

In order to distract themselves from the Falklands War the British mainly watched *Dallas*, asked each other who shot JR and finally agreed it had all been a dream.

The other thing Mrs Thatcher invented were Yuppies. They were like Nimbys and Dinkys and Hoodies but funnier. They drank champagne and wore red braces and shouted 'Sell! Sell! Sell!' down their giant immobile phones in restaurants and were often called Adrian or Hamish. (They were also frequently caught gentrifying London's backwaters.)

The 1990s

The most bestest thing that happened right at the beginning of the 1990s was that Horatio Nelson Mandela was Free At Last. Nelson forgave everyone for treating him and other black people so badly under Apartheid (which means if you're black, you can't go anywhere or do anything in South Africa except pick fruit that no one outside South Africa will buy, because they hate you). He forgave them so much that he offered to be President (a job absolutely no one else wanted by then) and they grovellingly accepted. There was a universal outpouring of love for Nelson, but not so much for his lovely wife Whinnie, even though she gave many of his supporters rubber necklaces as a thank-you present. At his inauguration, Nelson famously danced with the renowned balletician Desmond Tutu. Nelson will always be remembered as not only a Great Statesman but also Extremely and Way Cool.

Slightly less excitable, but no less excruciating, was the accession of John Major-Minor to the British Premiership League. John Major-Minor was known for being unknown, and remained so throughout his reign. He was probably a Conservative, although Edwina Curried-Eggs had an affair to do with him and may disagree. (We are now in the territory of the still-alive and have to be a bit careful in casting our aspersions as wildly as possible.)

Operation Dessert Storm was launched by the Americans when Iraq (led by Saddam Hussein) decided to invade Kuwait. Actually, no one really cared – or even knew – about Kuwait until now when Saddam started a talent show where he got British and American people living in Kuwait to be videoed making a convincing case why he shouldn't kill them. This led to 'Briton's Got Talent', 'The Ex-Factor' and other off-shoots such as 'Britons Come Dancing on Ice/Hot Coals/The Voice, and all very Strictly.'

Howsoever, the British soon joined the Americans in Operation Mission Creep. This war is still going on in my Living Memory and I think any comment by myself would be tendentious in the extremities, which nobody likes.

On the bright side, the 1990s invented:

- ✋ Mad Cow Disease;

- ✋ Royal Divorces. (These had hardly never happened before, but have probably started a fad. Hopefully Royals will be allowed to marry their second choice in the first place in future.);

- ✋ The Internet. (Mum says that in the old days, when you wanted to tell someone something, you had to write a letter, phone them, or even go and talk to them in the face. Also, when you wanted to watch a kitten skateboarding, you had to buy an actual kitten and wait until it actually did it.)

The 21st Century

It's worth noting that not everyone was looking forward to the 21st century beginning (except for Annie Lennox). Because Everyone was worried about The Millennium Bug. The Millennium Bug, people were told, might Eat Up History and refuse to allow The Future to continue. Lots of people spent lots of money trying to avert the possibility of the Millennium Bug taking over the world at midnight on the changing of the guard between the centurions. Fortunately, the Millennium Bug turned out never to have existed in the first place and everything was OK.

The other thing that happened in the main part of History in Briton in the early 21st century was a complete and utter outbreak of Foot-In-Mouth-Disease. This clearly ruined many farmers, but more politicians. By the spring of 2004, the future was fairly safe, which is good because...

My Complete and Utter History of the World ends just when my own History begins, for I, Samuel Stewart, aged 9, Mini-Historian, was born at 6.31 am on 2 March, 2004.

Of course, things that have happened since I have been alive will be remembered by me slightly differently from how other people will remember them, so I can't give such an impartial and objectionable view of them as I have in this book, where I have stuck to Complete and Utter Facts. (For example, Mrs Cooper and I have vastly different memories of the incident with the wasp in her couscous that Chardonnay definitely put there.)

It's interesting to think that even now, Today, will be History Tomorrow. So really we are all living in History all the time. In fact, History goes right up to Yesterday, though we won't know for a bit which were the events which were important enough to be considered Proper History for a long time (probably about a month). Like Great Granddad and the newspaper, but more so, you have to be quite a long way away from History before you can see it properly.